INVADERS

BY DANNY PEARSON

ILLUSTRATED BY
ALEKSANDAR SOTIROVSKI

FULL FLIGHT

Titles in the Full Flight Adventure series:

Planet Talent	David Orme
Invaders	Danny Pearson
Alien Exchange	Melanie Joyce
Camp Terror	Craig Allen
White Water	Jane A C West
Infinity Mirror	Roger Hurn
Robot Rampage	Jillian Powell
Stone End Stadium	Richard Taylor
Weed Killers	Jonny Zucker
Dynamite Deputy	Barbara Catchpole

Badger Publishing Limited
Oldmedow Road, Hardwick Industrial Estate,
King's Lynn PE30 4JJ
Telephone: 01438 791037

www.badgerlearning.co.uk

2 4 6 8 10 9 7 5 3

Invaders ISBN 978-1-84926-555-3

Publisher: Susan Ross
Senior Editor: Danny Pearson
Series Editor: Jonny Zucker
Designer: Fiona Grant
Illustrator: Aleksandar Sotirovski

CONTENTS

New words:

creature	detention
wrestling	flickered
species	nervously
Prime Minister	enormous

Main characters:

Mark

Liz

CHAPTER 1

What is That?

Mark slowly walked back home from school. It had been a very long day.

As he walked, he could see something move in the park bin in front of him.

What is that? Mark thought to himself. He went over for a closer look.

Inside the bin he could see a small creature wrestling with a burger wrapper.

'Wow,' gasped Mark. He had never seen anything quite like it.

It seemed friendly, so he carefully picked it up.

It had beautiful smooth fur, and a small round face.

The creature giggled and smiled.

Mark had to take this thing home. It was the coolest thing he had ever seen. He slipped it into his bag and hurried home.

"Dinner is ready," shouted Mark's Mum as he ran up the stairs to his room.

"OK, Mum!" he yelled back. "I will be down in a second!"

He quickly ran to his wardrobe, where he had an old hamster cage stashed. "There you go," Mark whispered to the creature. "This will do for now."

The next day Mark checked on the little creature before he went to school. It was curled up in a ball fast asleep.

"Perfect," said Mark quietly. "I will see you later little guy."

CHAPTER 2

More

Mark raced back from school.

He couldn't wait to check up on his new pet.

As he entered his room he saw that the wardrobe was wide open and the cage was laying open.

"Oh No!" Mark cried. "It has escaped!"

Suddenly he could see the bin next to his desk fall over. Out rolled five little creatures!

All of them bounced over to Mark and stood upright in front of him.

"What is going on? I need help," Mark said to himself. "I can't call Mum, she will go crazy. I know, Liz! She will know what these things are."

Liz was Mark's friend from school who knew everything about every animal.

Mark got on his mobile. "Liz, I need you to come over now," he pleaded.

"Why what is up? Are you OK?" She replied.

"I'm fine, I think, but I need you to come over," said Mark.

"I found a strange creature in the park and now there are more of them and I don't know what they are or what to do with them."

"Wow strange creatures!" Liz shouted. "I will be there in five minutes."

CHAPTER 3

Ground Control

"Mark, I have no idea what these things are," Liz said as she stared at the small, furry creatures. "You said they escaped from this cage?"

"Yes, but I have a lock on it now so they shouldn't be able to again."

"OK, well I think we should find a way to keep an eye on them while we are at school tomorrow. Maybe I can find something about them in the library or online," said Liz, whilst still staring.

"I'll set up my webcam, we can check on them from my phone," boasted Mark as he set it all up.

At school the next day they constantly checked the webcam in Mark's room from his phone.

It was the last lesson and they checked one last time on his phone.
There was no sign of movement.

"Everything seems to be OK today. I knew they wouldn't be able to break that lock."

The wardrobe door burst open.

"OH NO!" yelled Mark.

"Mark!" shouted his teacher. "What is going on back there?"

"Nothing Miss," he nervously answered.

"Nothing? Well that's detention for you tomorrow," she snapped back at him.

The school bell went and Mark and Liz shot back to his house.

On the way back they checked his phone. They could see that there were lots more of the creatures.

They were picking up objects and taking them apart.

One went right up to the webcam, smiled, then the camera switched off.

"I do not like the look of this," Liz said.

Mark and Liz burst into his room. All of the creatures stood up and stared at them in silence.

"Hello," came a voice from the desk.

They both spun around to look.

"Hello, we hope you don't mind but we used your Earth machine to learn your language," said one of the creatures.

"My computer?" asked Mark.

"Yes that is it, your computer," giggled the creature. "We haven't seen one as basic as that in a very long time."

"What is that?" questioned Liz, pointing at a strange object standing next to it.

"This little lady is what you call a satellite. We made it to contact our home to inform them that we will need a few more of us to come along and help with our work," the creature answered.

"Help to do what?" asked Mark.

"We cannot tell you just yet," laughed the creature. "But we have contacted your leader and someone will be round shortly to pick us up."

"Leader?" Liz and Mark both said.

There was a knock at the door.

They ran down to answer it.

In front of them stood three large men wearing suits and sunglasses.

"Hello, you must be Mark and Liz," one said calmly. "We are here to escort the aliens."

"Aliens?!" they both cried.

CHAPTER 4

Cleaners

They were shown into the back of a stretched car. The aliens raced into the back with them.

"Budge up," said one of the aliens.

They could see the TV screen in the car.

The aliens had sent out a message to all of the world's news stations.

They explained that they had come in peace and that they would need to speak to the world's leaders before they could start their work.

"What is this work you keep talking about?" asked Liz.

"We cannot tell you yet!" the aliens shouted.

The car pulled up outside a huge building. The large men tried to lead Mark and Liz away but the aliens insisted they came along too.

"We like them, they are to stay with us," they said together.

"Very well," grunted one of the guards.

They were led to a large room where they were told to wait.

A figure appeared in front of them. "Hello, I am here to discuss what it is you are after," it said.

The figure moved into the light.

It was the Prime Minister.

"We are not after anything Sir, we just wish to clean your planet," replied one of the aliens.

"Clean our planet?" questioned the Prime Minister.

"Yes Sir, we need you to tell everybody that we need a few weeks," the alien said with a smile. "We travel through space cleaning other species' mess, and you humans do leave an awful mess."

"And what are we meant to do whilst you 'clean up' Earth?" said the Prime Minister.

"We shall move you all to a holding area whilst we go to work," the alien answered.

"A holding area?" laughed the Prime Minister. "I don't think the human race will like being held prisoner."

"You humans should have thought about that before you wrecked your planet," the creature said with anger in its voice. "You either leave with us, willingly, or we force you off!"

"Force us off? And how do you intend to do that little one?" joked the Prime Minister.

Mark could see around his feet that the creatures all looked very angry. They all started to shake.

"Prime Minister, I would do what they say," pleaded Liz nervously. "They seem pretty smart and I don't think we should make them angry."

"HA!" laughed the Prime Minster. "No bunch of small, fluffy aliens are going to tell us what to do."

Just then the aliens let out a loud scream. They started to grow.

They grew past Liz and Mark to become enormous.

One of them stood in front of the Prime Minister, towering over him.

"By force it is," smiled the alien as it looked down on him.

CHAPTER 5

Holding Area

In a flash Mark and Liz found themselves surrounded by hundreds, thousand, millions of people.

They looked up to see a sky full of bright stars through a dome roof.

"Urm Liz, where are we?" asked Mark.

A giant screen flickered on, to reveal one of the alien's faces.

"People from the planet Earth," it announced, "we have been forced to move you all to a newly built holding area on your moon. Here you will stay while we clean up the mess you have made."

"We hope you enjoy your time here and we suggest that you use this time wisely. Learn to get along with one another and try to think of new ways to look after your planet.
We should only need about two weeks."

"I don't think I have to worry about that detention anymore," joked Mark.

"Mark this is serious," snapped Liz. "We have been dumped on the Moon!"

Mark laughed, "yeah but you just heard, it is only for two weeks, it could be fun."

The alien spoke again, "Sorry, it looks as if this will be a bigger job than we first thought. We should be back to pick you up and return you to your nice, clean, new planet in a few months... maybe a year... goodbye."

Mark and Liz looked at one another, "NOOOOOOOOO!!!"

Interesting Junk Facts

- *The world's annual consumption of plastic has increased from around 5 million tonnes in the 1950s to nearly 100 million tonnes today.*

- *Plastics can take up to 400 years to break-down in a landfill.*

- *If you lined up all the polystyrene foam cups made in just 1 day they would circle the Earth.*

- *In 2004, the UK sent 744 million Christmas cards; if they were all recycled, it would have saved 248,000 trees.*

- *Oil accounts for a quarter of all pollution incidents; one can of oil poured onto a lake can cover an area the size of two football pitches*

- *Almost half of the contents of our dustbins could potentially be recycled.*

- *In 1 year there would be enough waste in the UK to fill dustbins stretching from the Earth to the Moon.*

NASA Report

Scientists from NASA believe that, from a long distance, the changes in Earth's temperature could be seen as a serious threat made by an out-of-control civilisation.

In the report, entitled Would Contact with Extraterrestrials Benefit or Harm Humanity? *NASA outlines a list of outcomes which could occur were aliens to land on our planet.*

In the best case they suggest we will be able to swap information with the aliens that would stop poverty, hunger and disease. However, they may decide to do the opposite, which would see the destruction of Earth.

Questions about the Story

- *Where did Mark hide the first alien?*

- *How many aliens fell out of his bin on the second day?*

- *What had the aliens built?*

- *Where had all of the humans been moved to?*

- *How would you feel if you had been moved to the Moon?*

- *What would you do if you found one of these aliens in your bin?*

Lettuce Grows on the Ground

Anne Rooney

Editor: Alexandra Koken
Designer: Melissa Alaverdy
Educational consultants:
    Jillian Harker and
    Heather Adamson

Copyright © QED Publishing 2013

QED Publishing
A Quarto Group company
The Old Brewery,
6 Blundell Street,
London,
N7 9BH

www.qed-publishing.co.uk

ISBN 978 1 78171 209 2

A catalogue record
for this book is
available from
the British Library

Printed in China

Words in **bold**
can be found in
the Glossary on
page 24.

Contents

What is lettuce?

Lettuce is a leafy plant.

Roots hold it in the dirt.

We eat the leaves.

Other leafy
plants we eat are
spinach, cabbage
and sprouts.

cabbage

spinach

sprouts

Planting lettuce

Lettuce grows from tiny seeds. Plant the seeds in rows.

seeds

Lettuce needs room to grow. Pull out or snip some of the little plants.

Growing up

Lettuce grows in summer. It needs sunlight and lots of water. It droops when it gets too dry. It dies if it gets too cold.

A world of their own

Some people grow lettuce in **cold frames**. It protects plants from wind, frost and pests.

Farmers use long
plastic tunnels over
their plants.

Who likes lettuce?

Rabbits and **slugs** eat lettuce.
So do snails and birds.

rabbit

Butterflies lay
eggs on lettuce.
The eggs turn
into caterpillars.
They eat
the plants.

caterpillar

Shapes, sizes and colours

Some lettuce grows its leaves packed in a ball shape. This is called a "head".

Other lettuce grows in loose leaves.

Lettuce can be green, white, red or purple.

Some have frilly leaves.

15

More lettuce later

If not picked, lettuce grows a long **stalk** with flowers.

flowers

The flowers make
seeds. The seeds
fall on the dirt.
They grow into new
lettuce plants.

17

Good for you

Lettuce gives us **fibre**, **vitamins**, minerals and water. It has no fat.

Dark green and purple
lettuce taste stronger than
pale lettuce. They have
more vitamins and fibre.

Ready to eat

Pick lettuce heads when
the middle is firm. Use a
knife to cut the base.

Loose-leaf lettuce grow more leaves if some are cut off.

Tasty!

Some lettuce has a thick **stem** in the leaves. The stems are stir-fried in Chinese food.

stem

Lettuce can be used in salads.
It also tastes good in
a sandwich.

Glossary

cold frame an enclosure with a roof that lets light in. It is used to grow plants

fibre the part of a plant that helps other food to move through the digestive system

root part of a plant that grows under the ground and collects water and nutrients

seed part of a flowering plant from which a new plant can grow

slug a slimy creature that looks like a snail without a shell

stalk the main stem of a plant from which the leaves and flowers grow

stem the stiff, sticklike part that runs through the leaf of some lettuce

vitamin one of the nutritious parts of food that keeps bodies healthy